MY BOOK OF
Counting

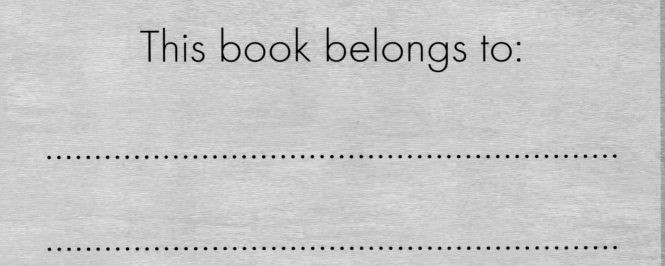

This book belongs to:

···

···

Illustrated by **Britta Teckentrup**

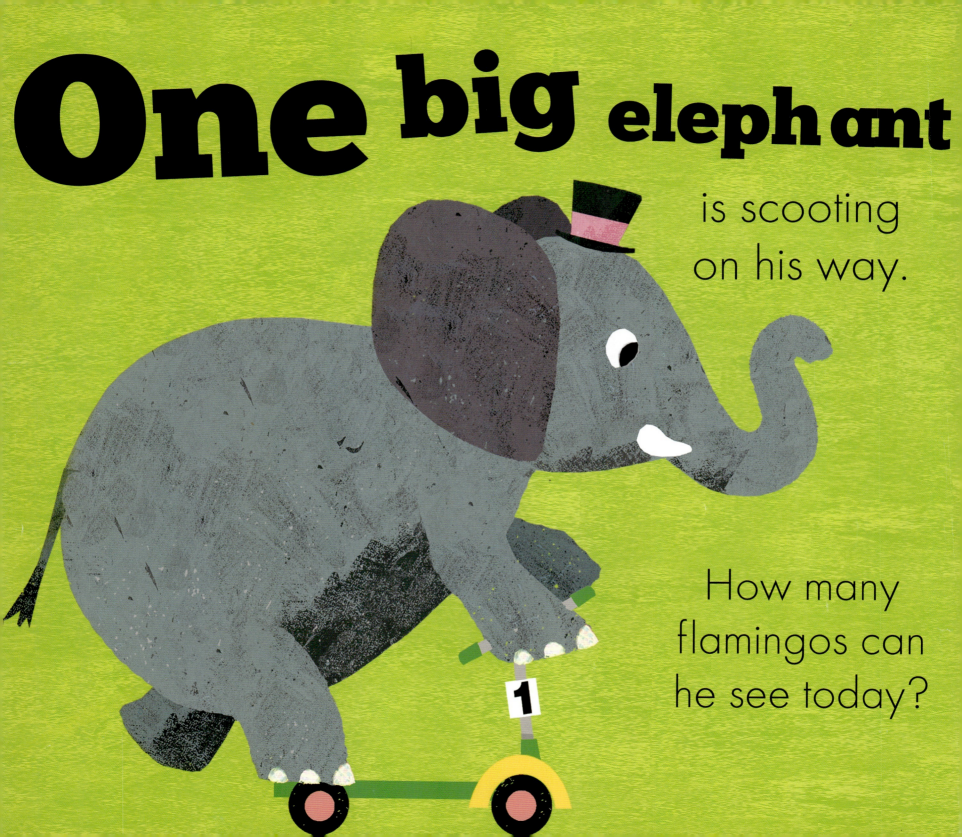

One big elephant

is scooting on his way.

How many flamingos can he see today?

Two cuddly pandas

are zooming
all around.

How many
crocodiles can
be found?

2 2 2 2

2 2

2 2 2

2 2 2

2 2 2

2 2 2

Three little pigs

are digging happily.

How many buzzy bees can they see?

Four tall giraffes

are racing through the town.

How many yaks are hanging around?

Five cheeky

monkeys are as busy as can be.
How many cheetahs can they see?

Six hoppy frogs are speeding on their way.

How many ducklings can they see today?

6 6

6 6

6

6

6 6

Seven perky
penguins

ring their fire bells.

How many tortoises are
peeping out of shells?

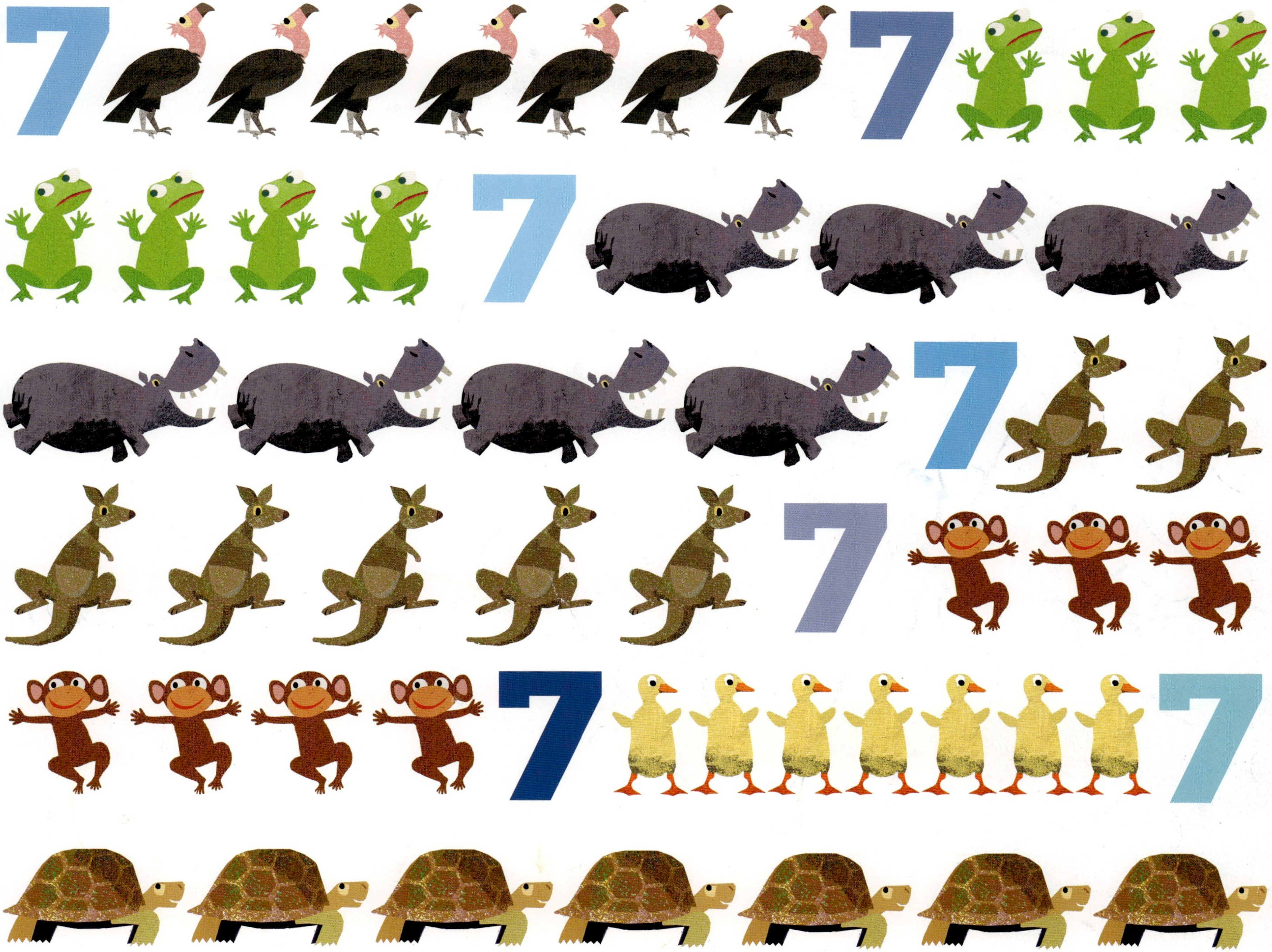
7
7
7
7
7
7
7

Eight happy cats

are whizzing far ahead.

How many butterflies are brightly coloured red?

Nine talking

toucans

are trundling on their way.

How many hippos are big, round and grey?

9

Ten noisy animals,

all creatures great and small,

riding on the yellow bus – can you count them all?

10

10 **10**

10

10